THE TERRIBLE TALES OF THE TEENYTINYSAURS!

For Mum, Dad, Susannah and Thomas

For their immense help and support during the making of this book,
I would like to thank Sarah McIntyre (you rule!), Stuart Pyle, Ashley
Fitzgerald, Helen Cherry, Woodrow Phoenix, Sybil Phoenix, Alex Milway,
Katie Lee, little Cecily and Milo, Lizzie Spratt, Jack Noel, Ben Norland,
Rosemary Canter, Jodie Marsh, Ellen Lindner, Stephen Betts, Dave Tebbutt
and especially my irrepressible and loveable knitjob Lauren O'Farrell -
thanks for being there, dude.

First published 2013 by Walker Books Ltd, 87 Vauxhall Walk, London SE11 5HJ

2 4 6 8 10 9 7 5 3 | Text and illustrations © 2013 Gary Northfield

The right of Gary Northfield to be identified as author and illustrator of this work has
been asserted by him in accordance with the Copyright, Designs and Patents Act 1988

Printed in China

British Library Cataloguing in Publication Data: a catalogue record for this book
is available from the British Library

ISBN 978-1-4063-3326-8

www.walker.co.uk

THE TERRIBLE TALES OF THE TEENYTINYSAURS!

GARY NORTHFIELD

WALKER

MEET THE GANG

REGGIE

Poor old Reggie was never the sharpest beak in the nest. But what he lacks in smarts, he makes up in loveliness. Everyone loves Reggie and Reggie loves them!

DAVE

Popular dude Dave is the natural leader of the pack. Always up for the next crazy adventure, his quick wit and ability to keep a cool head will get the gang out of the tightest of spots. Well, most of the time, anyway!

RONNIE

With his head stuck in daydreamy clouds, Ronnie prefers the company of butterflies and bees to the rowdy shenanigans of the other dinosaurs. That is, apart from the elusive girl of his dreams, Natasha, who unfortunately thinks he's a bit of a weirdo...

THOMAS

Loopy nut job Thomas is a long-necked engine of stupid energy! Never knowing when to stop, he'll either have you laughing at his mad antics, or screaming for him to stop being so annoying.

NATASHA

She might be the only girl in the gang but fiesty Natasha can definitely hold her own amongst the bolshy boys. In fact her brash manner has probably saved their sorry skins more times than they'd dare to admit.

CONTENTS

8

12

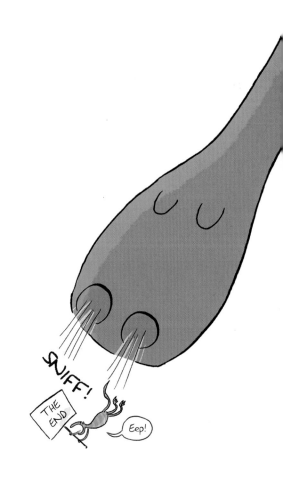

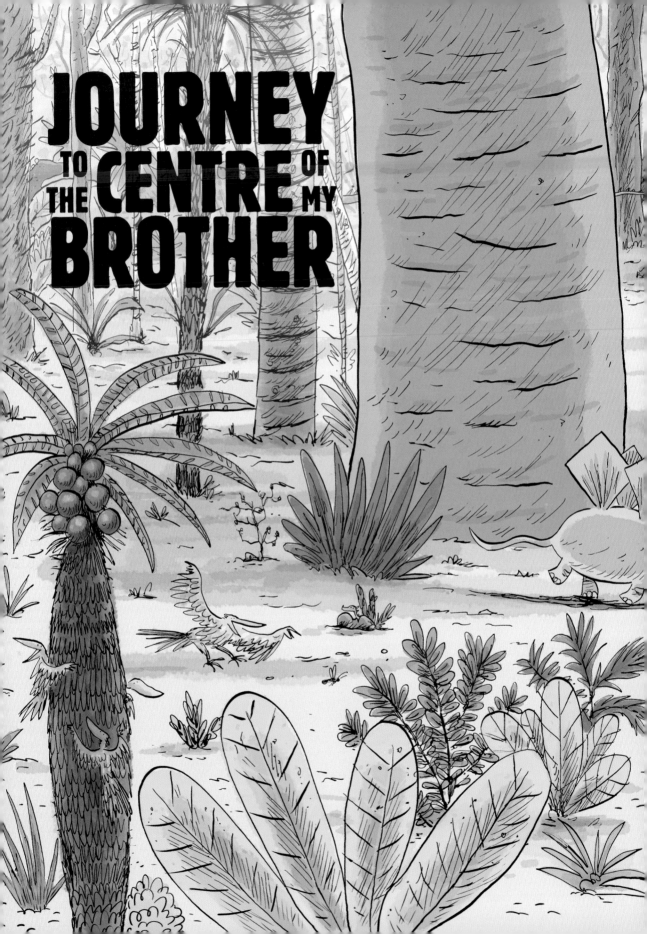

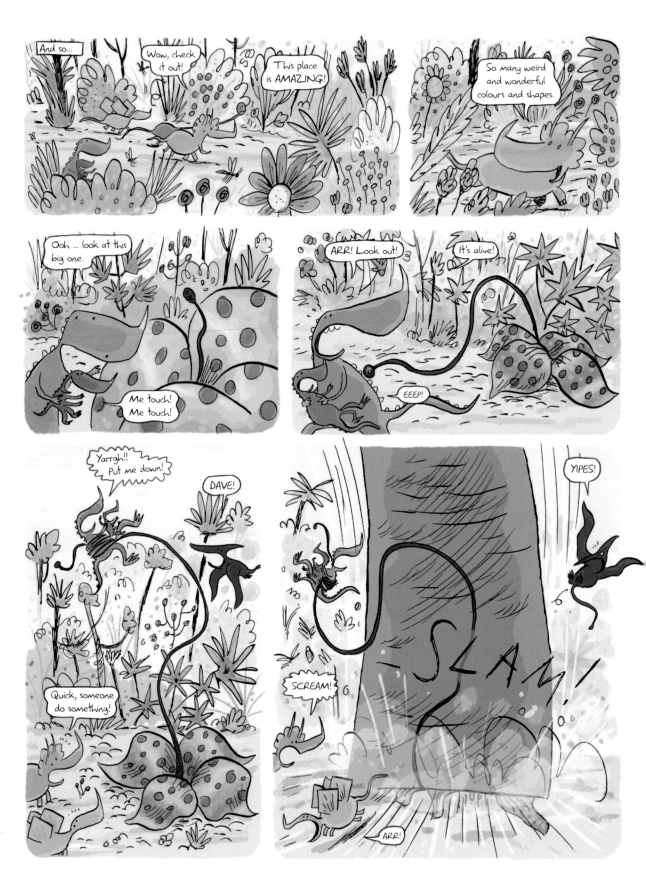

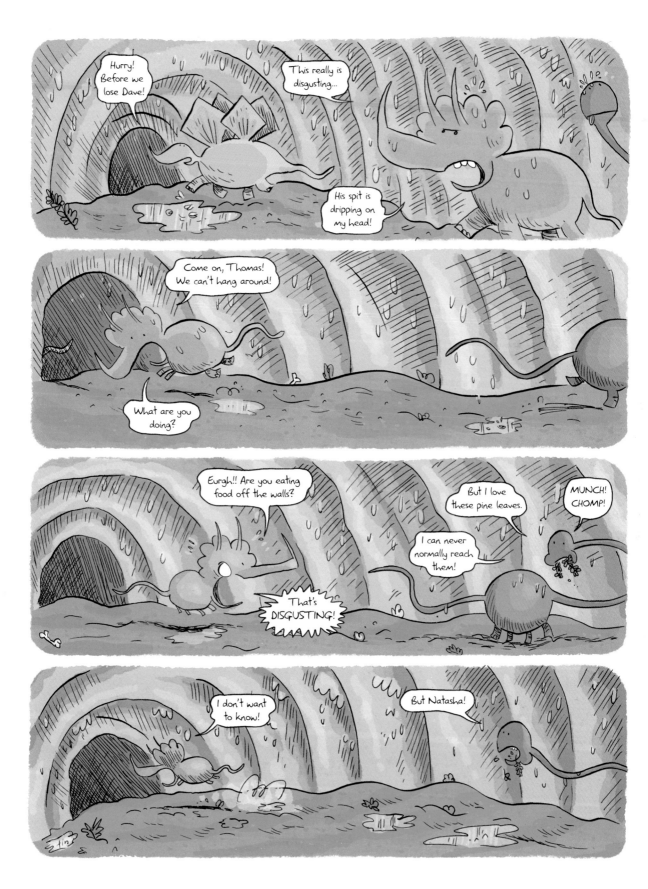

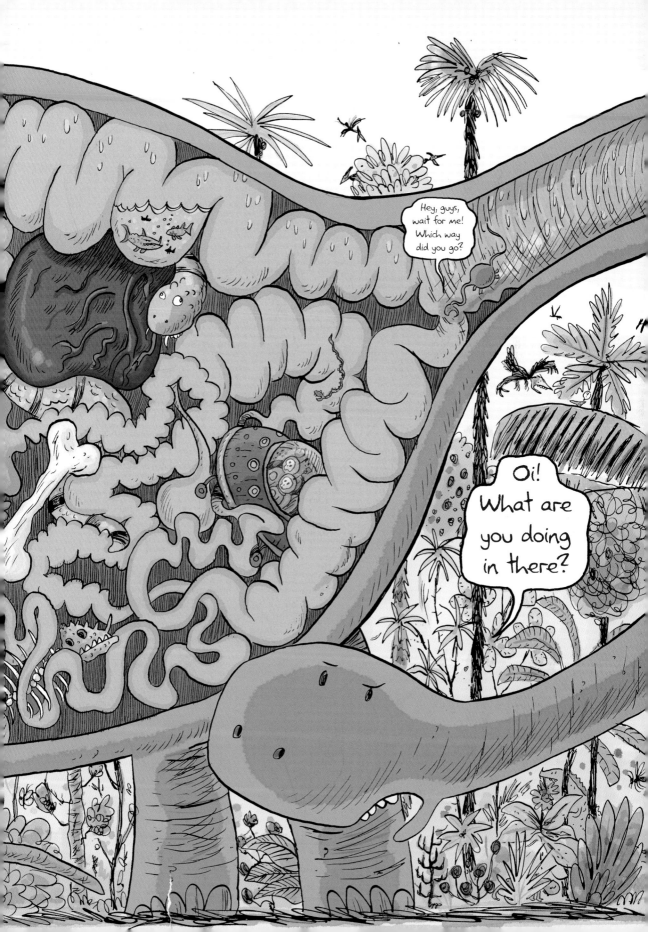

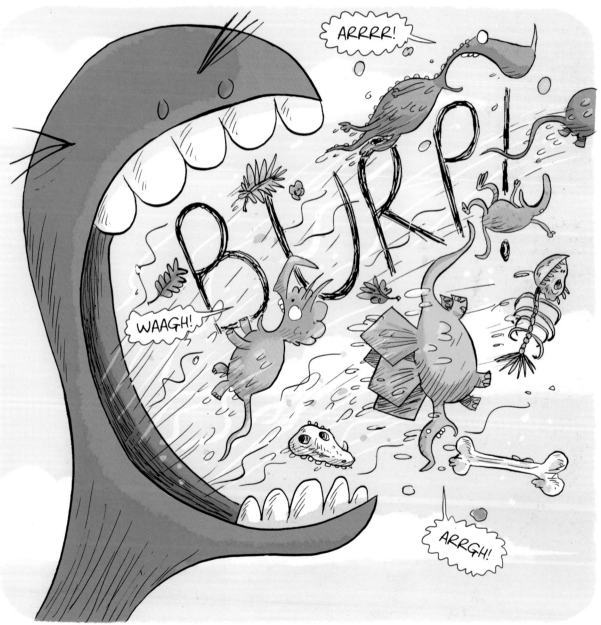

THE CLOUD WHISPERER

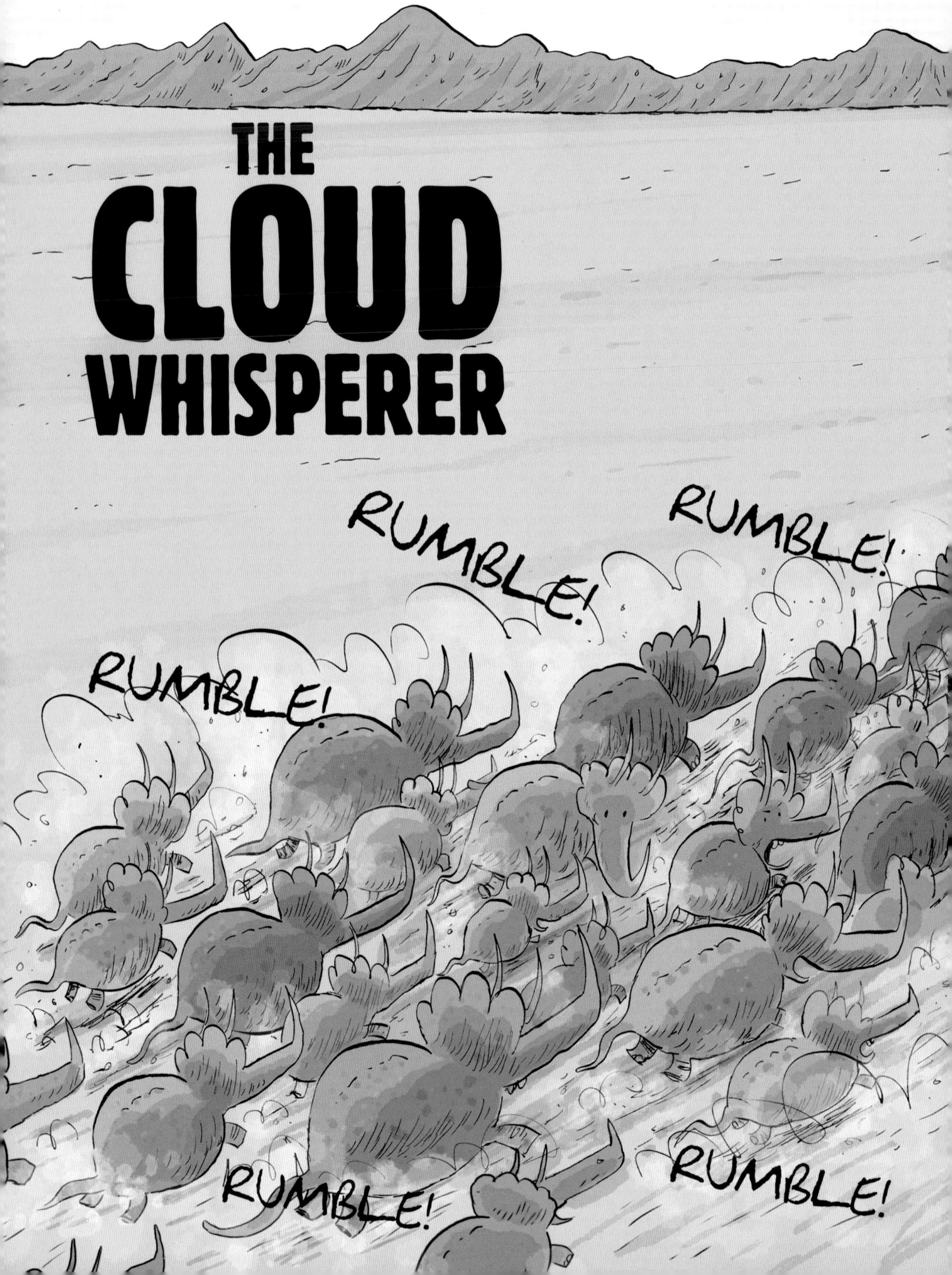

ONE GIANT SNEEZE
FOR DINO KIND

44

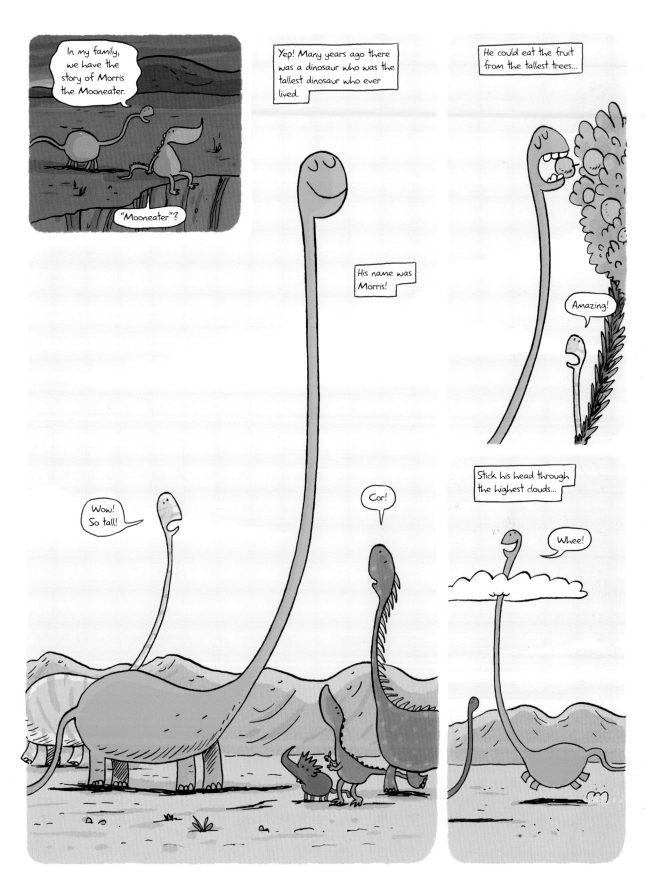

But it wasn't long before everyone noticed the moon growing back to normal.

And they felt really bad.

They tried to find Morris to apologize, but he was nowhere to be found.

But every month someone eats the moon, so maybe Morris is out there somewhere.

Boo hoo hoo! That is the saddest story I've ever heard!

Forget Morris, I want me some of that moon.

It sounds scrummy!

Look! It's really close to Headbutt Mountain.

We can totally reach it from there!

Woohoo! I can't wait to taste it!

I want to feel all that weird popping on my tongue.

Nnf!

It's too far away!

Hold still, Thomas, let me climb up your neck!

Oi!

Now lift up slowly...

Steady!

You're so flippin' heavy!

GNNNN!

I can't hold you much longer!

Sigh. It's no good. We need something taller.

How about your brother, Thomas? He's REALLY tall!

I don't know. He's got a bit of a cold at the moment.

47

This has to be the stupidest thing I've ever heard of, ever.

Sniff.

Come on, Colin! Imagine if we could actually lick the moon?

Come on, everyone! Climb up on each other's shoulders.

Gah! If any of my friends see me, I'm totally eating you all!

Hold it! Hold it! I'm nearly reaching it...

Arr! My neck!

Save me some moon rock!

Uh guys...

Arrgh!

What's he doing?

I think I'm going to sneeze...

UH...

UH...

CHOOO!

Eugh! That's so disgusting!

Wow! Your bogey flew for miles!

Hey. That gives me an idea.

What? Don't involve me, I've had enough of snot to last me a life-time!

SPLAT!

Can I go home now?

Oi!

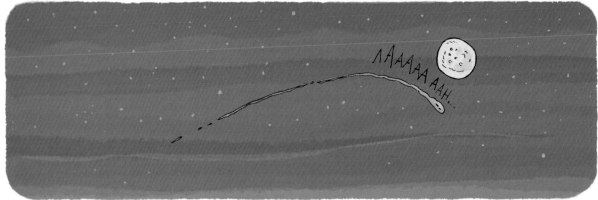

56

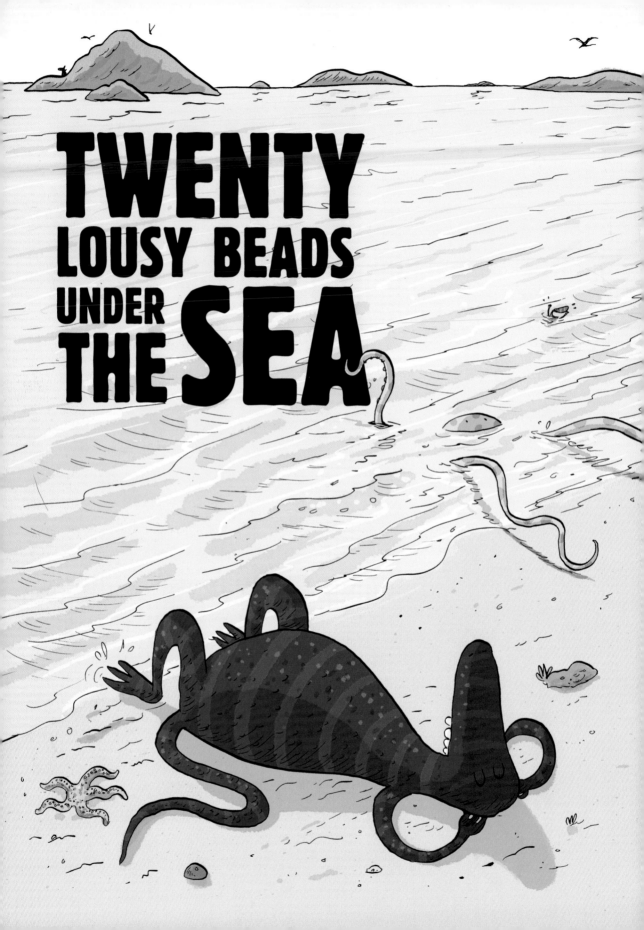

BZZZZ

72

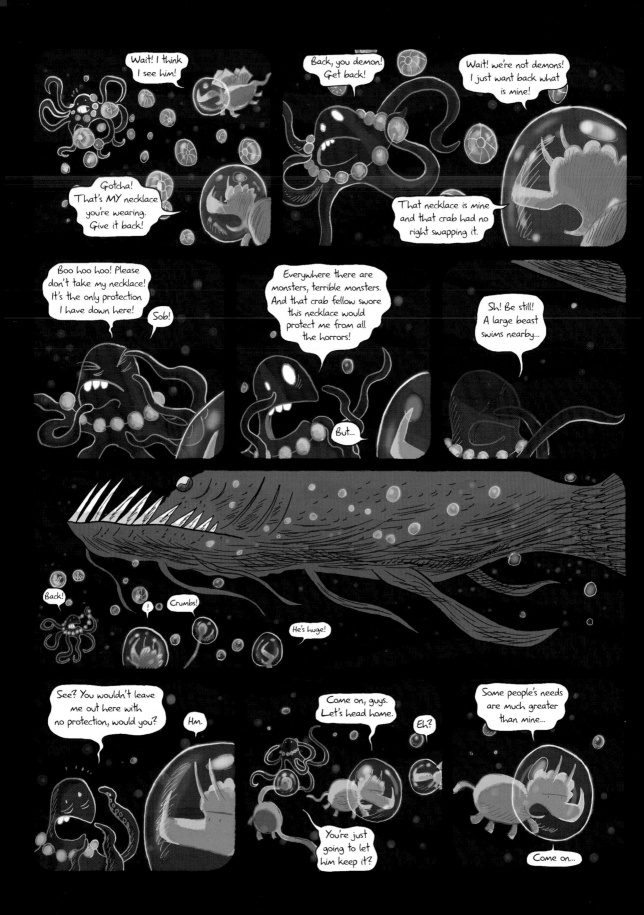

THE END...?

ABOUT GARY

Gary Northfield has been writing and drawing kids comics since 2002. He is most famous for Derek the Sheep, a comic-strip that appeared in *The Beano*. A collection of Derek the Sheep stories was published by Bloomsbury Children's Books. Gary has also created comics for *National Geographic Kids* magazine, *The Phoenix*, *The Dandy*, *The DFC*, *Horrible Histories* magazine, *Horrible Science* magazine and *The Magical World of Roald Dahl*. Gary loves dinosaurs. One day, with the profits from this book, he hopes to build a time machine so he can go back and see the jolly fellows with his very own eyeballs.